ISLAND OF SODOR

LAN
TLE

DEVIL'S BACK

Moey Road

Culdee Fell Summit

VICARSTOWN DIESELWORKS

VICARSTOWN

Blue Mountain Quarry

Rheneas

Lakeside

Skarloey

HENRY'S TUNNEL

Glennock

Ballahoo

Norramby

NORRAMBY BRANCH

Cros-ny-Cuirn

ANDING TONES

SODOR STEAMWORKS

Crovan's Gate

MAIN LINE

Kellsthorpe Road

Balladwail

Rolf's Castle

KIRK RONAN BRANCH

Sodor Bakery

Whiff's Waste dump

Kirk Ronan

N
W   E
S

This annual belongs to:

Kieran

Age:

10

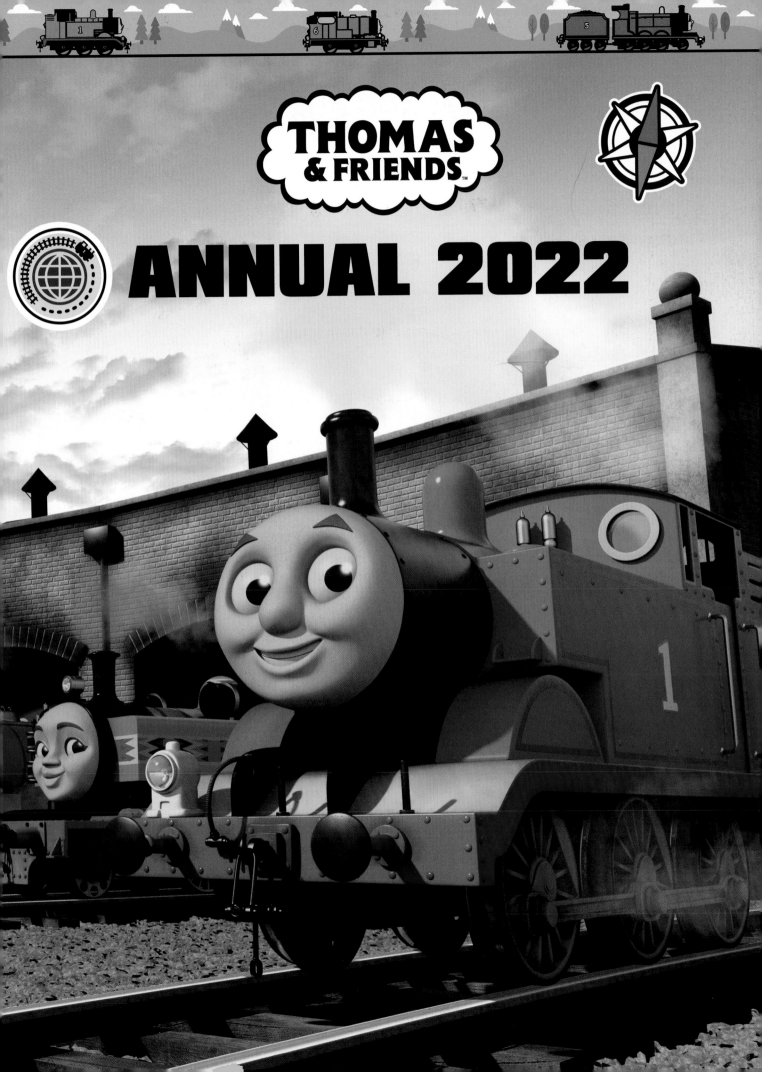

Farshore

First published in Great Britain 2021 by Farshore
An imprint of HarperCollins*Publishers*
1 London Bridge Street, London SE1 9GF
www.farshore.co.uk

HarperCollins*Publishers*
1st Floor, Watermarque Building, Ringsend Road, Dublin 4, Ireland

Written by Laura Jackson
Designed by Martin Aggett

CREATED BY BRITT ALLCROFT

ISBN 978 0 7555 0100 7
Printed in Italy
001

Contents

The Steam Team

Here comes Thomas!
The number 1 engine loves to help his friends and have big adventures around the world.

Here comes Percy!
Percy is Thomas' best friend. He is always cheerful and loves to deliver the mail on time!

Here comes Rebecca!
Rebecca is fast. Sometimes too fast! When she is not having bumps and scrapes, she loves to race her friends.

Here comes Nia!
Nia loves adventure, just like Thomas. She has travelled all the way from Kenya to be a member of the Steam Team.

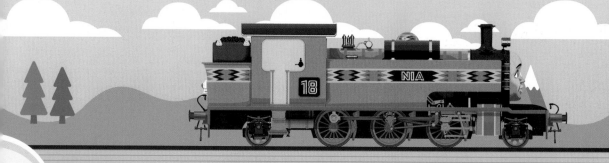

Coming Through

Here comes James!

James doesn't like getting dirty. He likes to show off his shiny red paintwork every day.

Here comes Gordon!

Gordon is a strong and powerful member of the Steam Team. He does pull the mighty Express, after all!

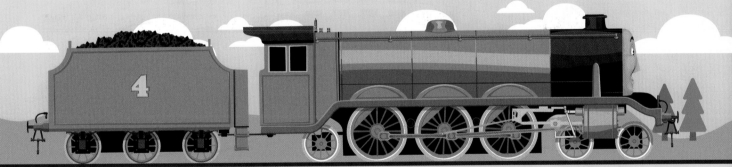

Here comes Emily!

Emily now has her very own number. Number 12! She loves to tell people what to do and how to do it.

Rainbow Rails

Help The Fat Controller bring rainbows to Sodor!

Use bright colours to finish the tracks.

red　**orange**　**yellow**　**green**　**blue**　**indigo**　**violet**

Let's give Thomas a new, shiny paint job too. Can you turn his steam into rainbow colours?

Rainbows make me smile!

How many colours are in the rainbow?

Answers on page 69

Hello, Cleo!

Cleo is a brand-new road engine on Sodor. She might be little, but she loves racing against the big engines!

I'm full of surprises!

Use a pencil to trace over Cleo's name.

Fun Facts

Paintwork: red

Loves: snow and racing fast

Cleo is... full of fun

Fun fact: Ruth built Cleo in her workshop

Mighty Memory

Here's Cleo enjoying her first ever snow day!

Talk about what you can see. Now cover up the picture and take the memory quiz.

1 What is Cleo carrying in her seat?

2 Which engine is looking at Cleo?

3 Are there are any passengers on the platform?

4 Is Gordon at the station?

5 What colour is the telephone box?

Answers on page 69

13

Say hello to the giraffes!

How many giraffes can you count?

It is hot and sunny in Kenya today.

I travelled to KENYA with Thomas!

What an adventure!

Draw a big tree to give Thomas some shade.

FINISH

Nia's Bright Idea

It was the morning of the Earl's Christmas party. The Engines had woken up to a very white Sodor.

"**Snow!**" peeped Emily. "The party at the castle will feel even more Christmassy now."

But it wasn't time to enjoy the party just yet. The Steam Team had *lots* to do.

James pulled a Christmas tree up to the castle, Gordon picked up passengers and Thomas dropped The Fat Controller at the Mainland.

Nia was busy too. She had arrived at Arlesburgh to pick up party lights. A tall building was flashing on the harbour.

"That's the lighthouse," said Skiff. "It helps ships safely find the harbour if it's dark or stormy. The crew can see the flashing light."

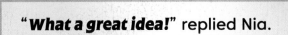

"*What a great idea!*" replied Nia.

All through the day, the snow fell thick and fast on Sodor.

When it was time to pick up The Fat Controller from the Mainland, Thomas couldn't plough through all the snow.

"There's only one way to collect The Fat Controller today," The Thin Controller told Thomas. "By air!"

Harold was ready in no time.

Whirr! Whirr! Whirr! went his blades in the sky.

Harold to the rescue!

It was nearly time for the party to start. The sky was turning dark and the snow was thicker than ever.

"*Must keep going, must keep going*," Nia puffed.

Then she noticed something in the sky. Harold! The wind had blown him the wrong way.

"Harold's in trouble!" Nia gasped. "He won't be able to see where to land."

She steamed off to get help.

Up at the castle, everybody was worried about Harold.

"If only we could guide him down somehow," said the Earl.

That gave Nia a big idea.

"The lighthouse!" she said. "Well, we don't have a lighthouse, but we have a big wheel. And lights!"

Quick as a flash, the Earl strung the party lights onto the wheel. It glowed brightly.

Whirr! Whirr! Whirr! Harold could see the lights from the sky! He finally landed safely with a little bump.

"Whoever's idea it was to light up the wheel is a hero!" said Harold.

"Glad I could be useful," blushed Nia.

The Fat Controller climbed out of Harold. He was dressed as Father Christmas! "This is why I usually travel by reindeer," The Fat Controller joked.

Everyone cheered for Father Christmas. But Nia got the biggest cheer of all, for saving the day with her bright idea!

Important Jobs

Everyone on Sodor has a job to do.

Draw lines to link up each friend to their Really Useful job.

a I fly to the rescue!

b I give out the Very Important jobs!

c I deliver the mail.

d I do the heavy lifting. Lift and load!

Which job would you like to do?

Answers on page 69

Girls to the Rescue

The girls are on their way to save the day!

Can you find the missing puzzle piece?

Say which letter piece fits into the space.

Answers on page 69

Hello, Nia!

Nia is the most colourful Engine on Sodor. Her patterns really make her stand out on the rails.

We're a good team!

Nia

Use a pencil to trace over Nia's name.

Fun Facts

Paintwork: orange with colourful patterns

Number: 18

Nia is... clever, brave and full of fun!

Top fact: she is from Kenya in Africa

Sodor Animals

Nia loves all the animals on Sodor.

Use the number line to help Nia count the different animals she meets today.

Answers on page 69

Point to the number in Nia's number line as you count each animal type.

Double Trouble

Crash! Splash! The Troublesome Trucks
have pushed Percy into the sea.
Can you spot five differences between these two pictures?

1

2

Answers on page 69

Imagine It!

Ruth needs help inventing a new vehicle for Sodor.

Use this drawing space to create your own amazing vehicle.

A Snowy Surprise

Whoosh! A snowstorm has covered Sodor.

Can you work out who has been hidden in the snow?

Draw lines to match up the friends.

1 Nia **2** Percy **3** Thomas **4** Emily **5** Bertie

Answers on page 69

Hello, Yong Bao!

Yong Bao will help anybody in trouble.

He is one of the bravest engines Thomas has ever met. Find out just how brave he is on page 60!

I'm as swift as a tiger!

Use a pencil to trace over Yong Bao's name.

Yong Bao

Fun Facts

Paintwork: red with a gold tiger

Works: on the Chinese railway

Yong Bao is... always ready for action!

Fun fact: he used to be blue

Animals Around the World

Yong Bao loves animals.

Can you draw a picture of
some animals that live
in your country?

Tigers
live in his
country!
ROAR!

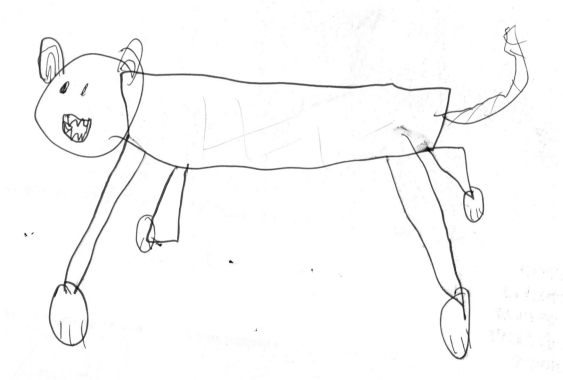

What
noises do
the animals
make?

James the Super Engine

It was a sunny day at Knapford Station. A group of children were busy showing James their favourite hero.

"**He's called Red Shadow**," the children giggled. "**He can fly at supersonic speed!**"

James was impressed. "I wonder if I have hero powers too ..." he thought.

He started to imagine what it would be like to be a hero. "**Rail Rocket to the rescue!**"

James was lost in his dream all morning. He didn't notice the track ahead.

Screech! Too late. James skidded into a bunch of oil drums.

CRASH!

SPLASH!

Thick black oil splattered over his face.

"***Oh no! My paintwork!***" he cried out.

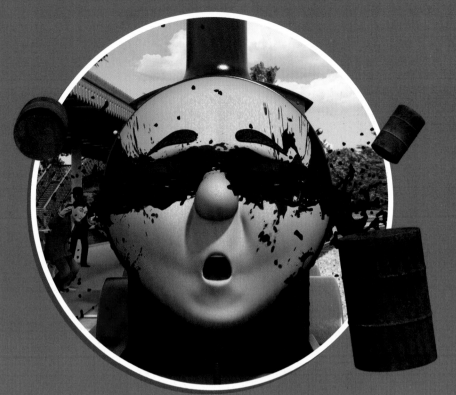

But as James steamed over Fenland Bridge, he saw something amazing in his reflection.

"***Blistering Boilers!*** I look just like ... ***Rail Rocket!***" gasped James. "Maybe I can be a hero."

Clickety-clack, clickety-clack!
James raced down the tracks,
looking for a real-life rescue.

"**Help!**" came a voice.

"An emergency!" puffed James.
"Never fear, Rail Rocket is here!"

But nobody needed rescuing. Some children had
got their kite stuck in a tree. James puffed steam
from his funnel and blew the kite down.

He just hoped his next call would be a real rescue.

Further down the track, a bell started to ring. **Ding-a-ling**.

"Did my super hearing detect an emergency bell?" James gasped. "*Rail Rocket to the rescue!*"

But it wasn't an emergency bell. It was some goats with bells around their necks.

"Oh, there's never anybody to rescue!" puffed James, crossly.

But James was wrong. Over at the Crosby Coal Hopper, Percy's brakes had broken. *He couldn't stop!*

CRASH!

Percy skidded off the rails. His trucks bounced and bashed into Rebecca and the coal hopper.

"**Help!**" shouted Rebecca. The coal hopper began to wobble above her. "I can't move!"

James heard the cries – this time it sounded like a real emergency.

Clickety-clack, clickety-clack! James ploughed through the broken trucks and pushed Rebecca to safety.

Just in time ...

CRASH! The coal tower toppled onto the tracks.

"Now I must fly," said James, in a cloud of coal dust. "**Sodor needs Rail Rocket!**"

With that, Rail Rocket vanished down the tracks.

"**Wow!**" gasped Percy. "Who is Rail Rocket?"

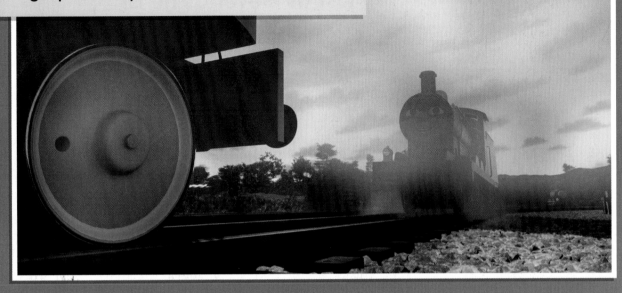

Later that night, Percy was telling everyone about the mysterious Rail Rocket.

"He was in disguise," said Rebecca. "He was a real hero."

James giggled to himself. Maybe you don't need superpowers to be a real-life hero after all!

Guess with Gordon

Show Gordon that you are just as clever as he is!

Take his fun Sodor quiz.

 Point to the BIGGEST animal.

 **Point to the BLUE engine.**

 **Point to the friend that can fly.**

 **Point to something you might take to the beach.**

Answers on page 69

I Can Write!

Brrr! Sodor is frosty today.

Use a pencil to trace over these winter words.

Start your pencil on the bigger dots!

snow   cold

ice   white

Now use your pencil to guide The Fat Controller along the icy paths. Try not to bump into the sides!

4.00   Win! is 4.00

0.00

START

Go Green!

Percy is a happy little engine.

Let's go green and colour him in.

You will need these colours

Now draw a happy yellow sun in the sky.

Rebecca Coming Through

Woah, Rebecca is moving fast today!
Use a pencil to race along the track with Rebecca.
How many friends does she steam past?

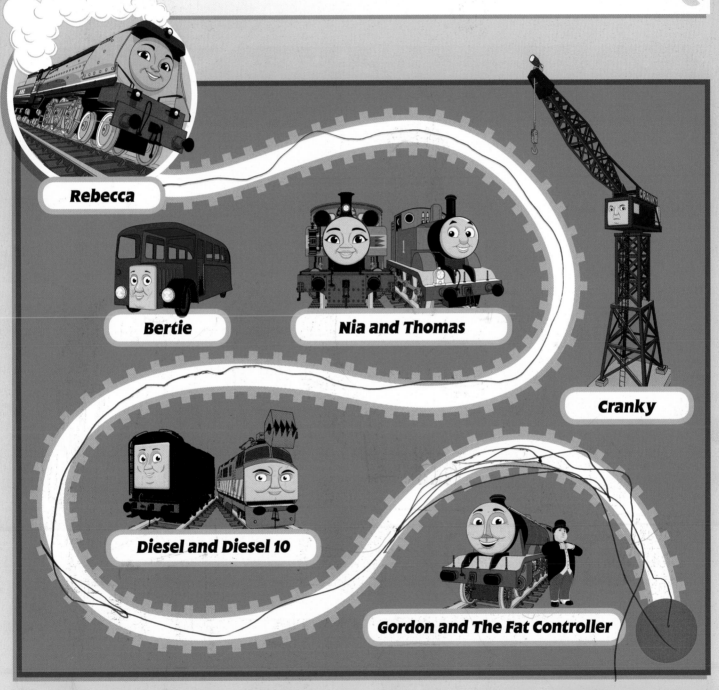

Rebecca

Bertie

Nia and Thomas

Cranky

Diesel and Diesel 10

Gordon and The Fat Controller

1 2 3 4 5 6 7 8 9 10

Answers on page 69

In the number line, point to the number of friends Rebecca passes.

Christmas Magic

Santa has sprinkled some Christmas magic on Sodor!

Can you spot five differences between these festive pictures?

Trace over one part of the snowman each time you spot a difference.

2

Answers on page 69

Brazil Boogie

A band are about to play a song for Thomas in Brazil!

Can you spot the close-ups in the big picture?

a

b

c

d

I travelled to BRAZIL with Thomas!

Now sing your favourite song out loud!

Answers on page 69

Hot and Cold

Which object goes with which weather type?

Drawn lines to link the objects to the hot and cold weather pictures.

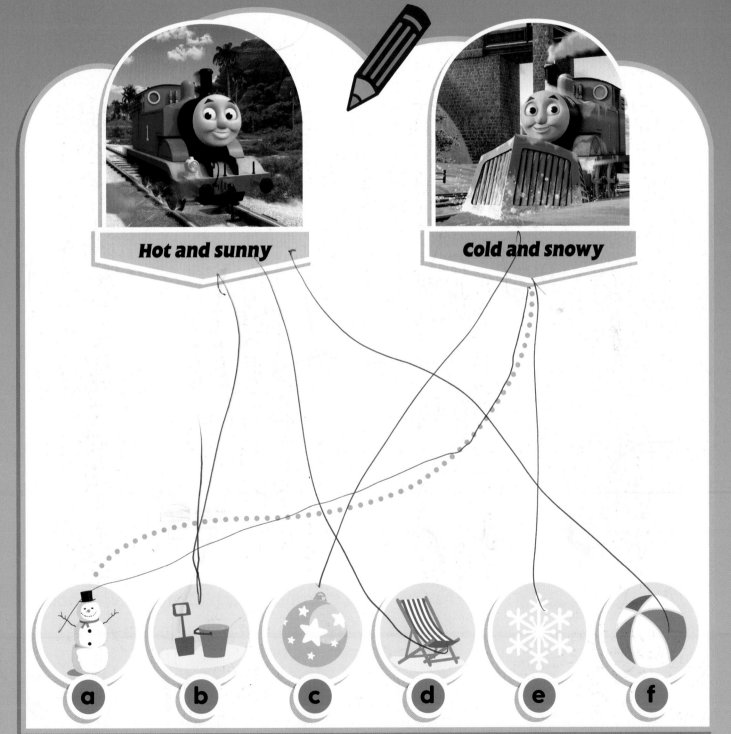

Hot and sunny

Cold and snowy

a   b   c   d   e   f

Answers on page 69

45

Big World Bunting

Look at all the colourful bunting Thomas saw in Brazil!

Would you like to make your own special bunting?

You will need:

★ your bunting pieces

★ scissors

★ crayons, paints or felt-tip pens

★ sticky tape

★ ribbon or string

Ask an adult to help.

How to make your bunting:

★ Ask an adult to help you cut out the bunting shapes on the opposite page.

★ Use your colouring pencils, pens or paint to decorate some of the pictures.

★ On the blank bunting shapes, you could draw your favourite engines.

★ Ask an adult to cut a length of string or ribbon.

★ Stick each bunting piece along the string or ribbon at even intervals.

★ Now hang up your Big World Bunting for everyone to see!

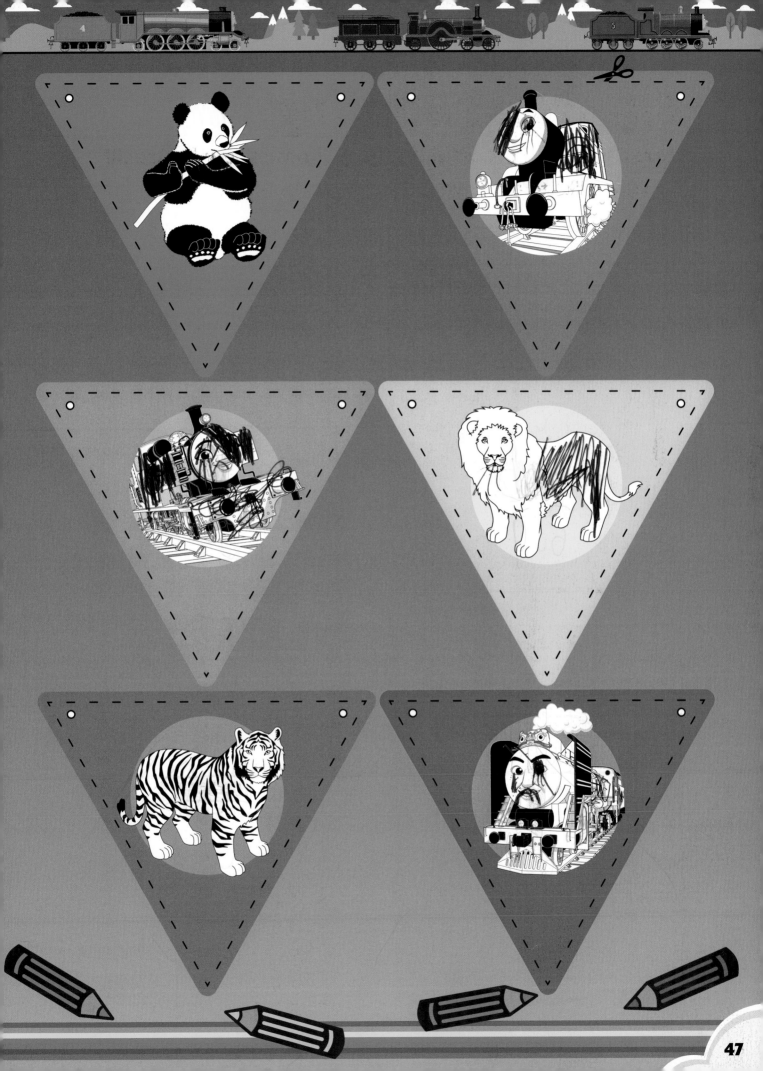

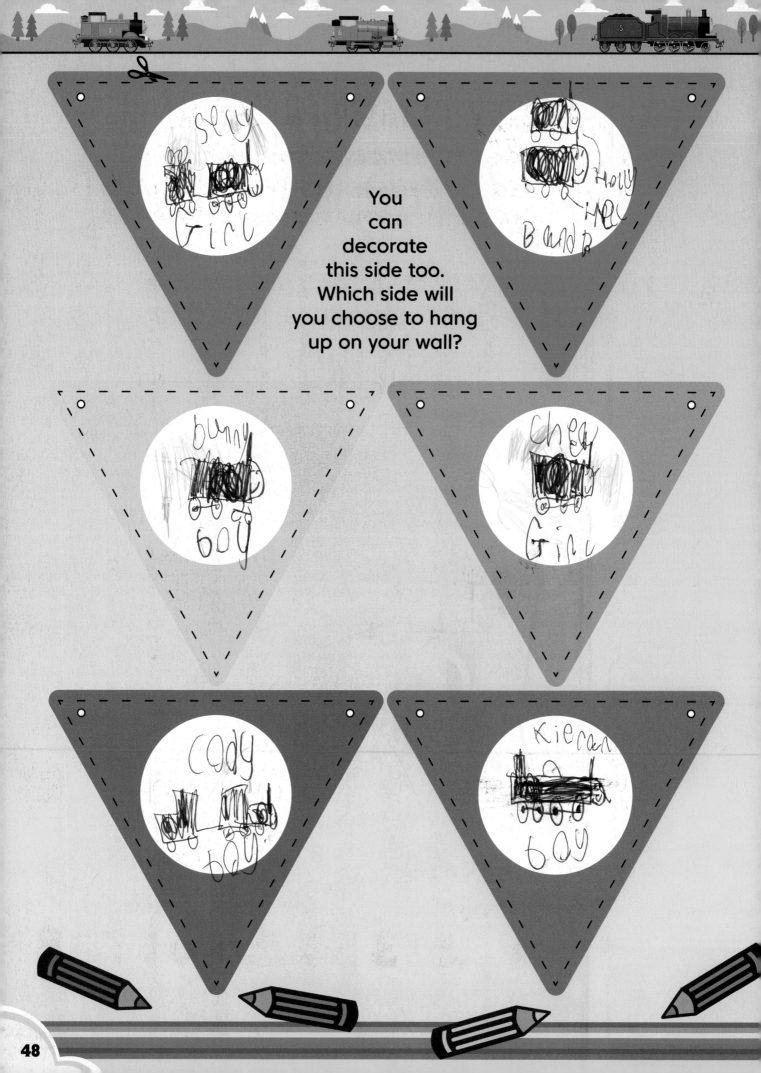

You
can
decorate
this side too.
Which side will
you choose to hang
up on your wall?

Catch Me If You Can

Gordon and Cleo are having a race!

Ask an adult to set a timer or count along as you play.

Put your pencil on the start and see how long it takes to complete each trail.

START

Cleo took

seconds.

START

Gordon took

seconds.

who was the winner?

Hello, Thomas!

The number 1 engine is kind, helpful and sometimes a little bit cheeky. He loves to explore the world and meet new friends. Adventure awaits!

Everyone is welcome on Sodor!

Use a pencil to trace over Thomas' name.

Thomas

Fun Facts

Paintwork: blue

Number: 1

Thomas is ... a Really Useful Engine

Fun fact: Thomas has met the Queen!

Engine in Disguise

Ashima is having a fancy-dress party in India. Thomas has dressed up as an elephant.

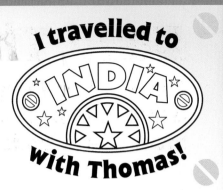

I travelled to **INDIA** with Thomas!

Can you guide him to Ashima to get the party started?

Start

Finish

Answers on page 69

Toot! Toot!

The engines are all ready to go. Colour in Thomas and then get spotting!

Things to spot:

girl

station clock

number 6

3 squirrels

toolbox

2 seagulls

Each time you spot something, shout out 'Toot! Toot!'

Answers on page 69

Emily to the Rescue

One sunny day, the Railway Safety Inspector came to do a safety test on Sodor ...

"When you hear a siren, whoever is closest to the **Search and Rescue Centre** must get to **Rocky**," said **The Fat Controller**.

The siren suddenly rung out, but ~~Emily~~ had to stop at a red signal. ~~Percy~~ steamed right through it. Naughty ~~Percy!~~

"**Rescue Engine coming!**" said ~~Percy~~. But his rails crossed into ~~Rebecca's~~ path. ~~Percy~~ couldn't stop ...

CRASH! ~~Percy~~, Rebecca and ~~James~~ all wanted to be the first engine to Rocky. But now they were completely stuck.

Meanwhile, **Emily** noticed Stone Bridge was crumbling. **It wasn't safe!** She steamed off to get ~~Rocky~~.

But while she was gone, ~~Gordon~~ got stuck under the bridge.

Smash! The bridge began to crumble!

Emily pulled **Rocky** to the bridge. He slammed up his crane arm to hold the bricks. **Clever ~~Emily~~ saved the day!**

Later, **The Fat Controller** gave ~~Emily~~ a number. **Number 12!** She was given a new job too – Sodor's first Safety Engine.

Well done, Emily!

Big World Quiz

Take Thomas' quiz to learn about his adventures all over the world.

I met some splashy elephants in India!

What colour are elephants?

- Grey
- Blue
- Green

What grows on palm trees?

- Monkeys
- Coconuts
- Frogs

I saw some very tall palm trees in India, too!

I saw a giant panda in China!

What do pandas eat?

- Chocolate eggs
- Bamboo
- Balloons

What is the weather usually like in a desert?

- [ ] Cold and snowy ❄
- [ ] Hot and sunny ☀
- [ ] Wet and rainy 🌧

I rescued a baby kangaroo in the desert in Australia!

I went to a very special beach in Brazil.

What might you see at the beach?

- [ ] A boat
- [ ] A giraffe
- [ ] A snowman

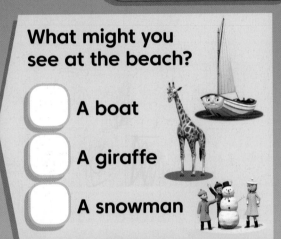

I travelled the world with Thomas!

1

Now tell Thomas a story about a fun place you have visited. What did you see there?

Yong Bao and the Tiger

When you see a picture, join in and say the word!

tiger  **Yong Bao**  **snow**  **tracks**

When used to be a blue engine, he saw an amazing thing one day in China. A stripy on the !

The stared at and stared at the .

"It's the most beautiful creature I've ever seen," thought . But as quickly as it had arrived, the had gone.

The next day, looked for the but he couldn't find it anywhere. Each day, would race along the searching for the . Days turned into months. Poor thought he would never see the again.

Winter came and covered the land. was busy chuffing up the mountain 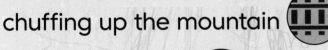 when he saw the !

The  **roared**, like it was trying to tell something.

"Do you want me to follow you?" asked.

The ran down the . followed. As they

turned a corner, saw a packed passenger engine sliding

towards the edge of the mountain. People were in danger!

Quick as a flash, coupled himself to the coaches.

Heave! Pull! kept slipping in the .

He looked up at the who gave a mighty **ROAR!**

found a burst of strength and heaved the carriages to safety.

Word soon spread about 's

bravery. He was given a new red paint

job and a emblem on his tender.

 never did see the again,

but he would never forget it.

My Important Engine

Yong Bao has a tiger on his tender.
What animal would you choose?

Trace over the dots to complete your very own
engine. Then draw an animal on the side.

Kieran

1912

Colour your engine with your best crayons!

64

Happy Christmas

Let's wish Thomas and his friends a Happy Christmas!

HAPPY CHRISTMAS

By ....

Write your name here!

Let's Explore

Thomas finds adventure outside in nature every day.

He loves to steam past the sea and through fields and towns in the sun, snow and rain! Can you spot any of these things when you are out and about this week? **Tick the boxes.**

	Bird		Sun		Dog		Squirrel
	Flowers		Cloud		Tree		Bus
	Boat		Rabbit		Sheep		Bridge

Now draw a picture of the best thing you saw this week!

Answers

Page 13
Mighty Memory
1. A snowman
2. Thomas
3. Yes
4. No
5. Red

Page 22
Important Jobs
a. Harold
b. The Fat Controller
c. Percy
d. Cranky

Page 23
Girls to the Rescue
Piece **b** is missing.

Page 25
Sodor Animals
2 cows
6 chicks
5 rabbits
3 chickens

Page 26
Emergency, Emergency!

Page 27
Double Trouble

Page 29
A Snowy Surprise
1e - Nia
2b - Percy
3a - Thomas
4c - Emily
5d - Bertie

Page 38
Guess with Gordon
1) Elephant
2) Thomas
3) Parrot
4) Bucket

Page 41
Rebecca Coming Through
Rebecca passes 8 friends.

Pages 42-43
Christmas Magic

Page 44
Brazil Boogie

Page 45
Hot and Cold
Hot and sunny: b, d, f
Cold and snowy: a, c, e

Page 53
Engine in Disguise

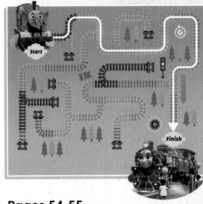

Pages 54-55
Toot! Toot!

Pages 58-59
Big World Quiz
1. Elephants are grey
2. Coconuts grow on palm trees
3. Pandas eat bamboo
4. The weather in the desert is usually hot and sunny
5. You might see a boat at the beach